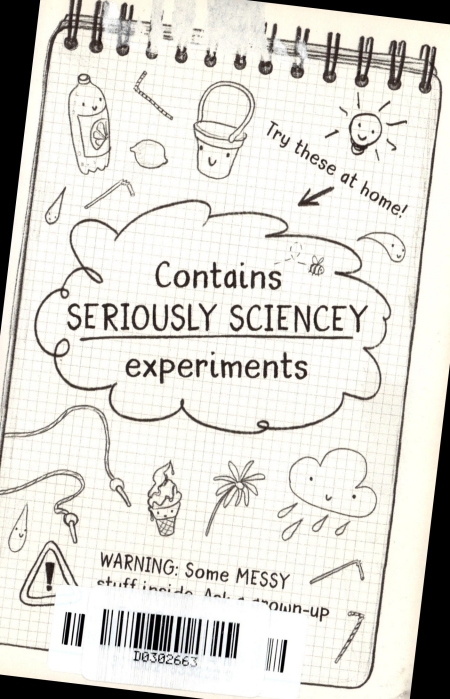

Try these at home!

Contains **SERIOUSLY SCIENCEY** experiments

WARNING: Some MESSY
stuff inside. Ask a grown-up

D0302663

BY **JANE CLARKE** ILLUSTRATED BY **JAMES BROWN**

 L'S AWESOME SCIENCE

Splash Down!

 FIVE QUILLS

Mrs Good

Mr Good

Precious

Also starring these guys!

To Ruth and Paul, with thanks for
all the science help! – J.C.

For Chris, Amber and Seth xxx – J.B.

AL'S AWESOME SCIENCE: SPLASH DOWN!

First published in Great Britain in 2018 by Five Quills
93 Oakwood Court, London W14 8JZ

www.fivequills.co.uk

Five Quills is a trademark of Five Quills

Edited by Natascha Biebow at Blue Elephant Storyshaping
Designed by Becky Chilcott

A CIP record for this title is available from the British Library

ISBN 978 0 9935537 4 5

1 3 5 7 9 10 8 6 4 2

Printed and bound in Great Britain by Clays Ltd, St Ives plc

CONTENTS

The Heat Is On!

Al Boffin peered through the eyeholes in the large cardboard box covering his head. His new experiment had begun!

He counted off the seconds on his watch. ". . . two hundred and ninety-eight, two hundred and ninety-nine, three hundred!" Al threw off the box and blinked in the sunlight. His freckly

face was all red and his hair was sticking up.

I have to cool this down! he thought. *Maybe this will help . . .*

He grabbed the roll of aluminium foil that he'd found in the kitchen drawer earlier and began to wrap the box in it. The corners were tricky.

"Mangled molecules!" Al muttered, as he tore and crumpled the shiny foil around them. He used up the entire roll. The box looked very roboty when he'd poked out the eyes! Al grinned. He picked it up and plonked it on his head.

The back door opened with a **CREEEAK** and Einstein, the Boffins' big, hairy dog, shuffled outside, followed by Mrs Boffin. Einstein glanced up at Al, but didn't seem to notice anything unusual about a boy wearing a box on his head. He slowly padded across to the empty paddling pool in the middle of the grass and stood there with his long, pink tongue hanging out.

"There's no water in it!" Al sighed. Einstein wasn't a genius, even if he was named after one. "Come and sit in the shade, you silly thing."

Al led Einstein into the shadow made by their next door neighbour's fence. Einstein lay down, panting.

Mrs Boffin squinted at the bright glare that bounced off the foil-covered box on Al's head.

"Nice hat," she said. "You need to put some of this on, too." She thrust a tube of sun cream at Al.

"In a hurry . . . got to get back to the shop . . . can't sell ice-cream fast enough today," Mum said in a rush. "Drink lots of water. Don't get up to anything messy . . . 'bye!"

"'Bye, Mum!" Al pulled the foil-covered box off his head and dropped it on the grass. He'd totally lost count of the number of seconds he'd been under it, so he'd have to repeat the experiment. He took the lid off the sun cream and rubbed some on his arms. It made him smell like coconut.

"Don't use all of it!" a voice said in his ear. "I need some, too!" Al's twin sister Lottie took the tube and slathered sun cream on her face and neck.

Al felt something slobbery on his arm. Einstein gave his elbow a big, sloppy lick, then threw himself on Lottie, licking her ears.

"He likes coconut," Al giggled as Lottie pushed Einstein away. Einstein wagged his tail and shuffled back off to curl up in the shade.

Lottie wiped the dog drool off one ear and glanced round the garden. "It's so dry," she said worriedly. "The plants will die if the drought goes on much longer." She carefully lifted a rose leaf and looked underneath it. "But bugs love it," she said, cheering up. "They hatch quicker in the heat so there are lots more about. Just look at all these spiders!"

Al shuddered. Lottie wanted to be a wildlife TV presenter when she grew up and she loved creepy crawlies. But he couldn't stand spiders.

Lottie let the rose leaf spring back into place. A blob of spider's web dropped onto Al's foil-covered box. "What are you up to?" she asked him.

"I'm working out what's the best covering for my time-machine

capsule," Al said. "It will need something to protect it from the very hot and cold temperatures as it travels through space and time. They use special foil in Space, so I'm experimenting with aluminium foil . . ."

Al picked up his box and brushed away the sticky glob of web that had stuck to it. A cluster of tiny spiders scuttled up his arm.

He screeched, tossing the box into the air.

YIKES!

Lottie grabbed Al's hand and hauled him over to the rosebush. "Hold still," she told him as she gently helped the tiny creatures onto the leaves. "You're upsetting the spiderlings!"

"What about them upsetting me?" Al squeaked. "They're disturbing my experiment." He picked up his box and held it at arm's length as he carefully checked it for spiders. Once he was sure it was bug-free, he put it on his head and began to count off the seconds.

"How's it going?" asked Lottie.

"It feels much cooler inside when the box is covered in foil," Al said happily as he removed the box. "The sun's rays must bounce off it." He took out his notebook and made a note. *Time machine needs protecting from very hot and cold temperatures when it travels through space and time. Cover the capsule in foil!!!*

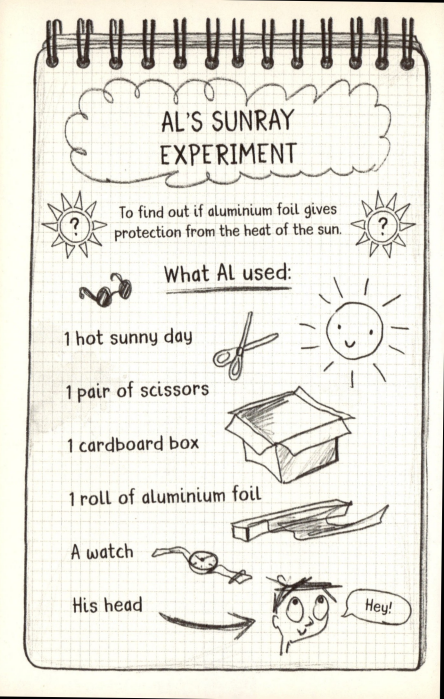

AL'S SUNRAY EXPERIMENT

To find out if aluminium foil gives protection from the heat of the sun.

What Al used:

1 hot sunny day

1 pair of scissors

1 cardboard box

1 roll of aluminium foil

A watch

His head

Hey!

What Al did:

He prepared the box by cutting off the bottom flaps and making eyeholes.

He stood in the sunshine, put the box on his head and timed five minutes on his watch.

Then he covered the box in foil and repeated the standing in the sunshine bit.

Results:

Al's head felt very hot inside the uncovered cardboard box.

When Al put on the foil-covered box, it felt much cooler.

Observations:

1. The uncovered cardboard box absorbed the heat from the sun.

2. The sun's rays bounced off the foil-covered box so it felt cooler inside it.

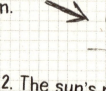

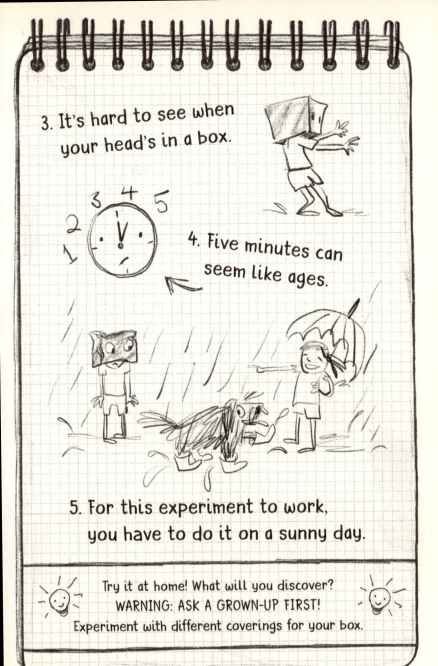

3. It's hard to see when your head's in a box.

4. Five minutes can seem like ages.

5. For this experiment to work, you have to do it on a sunny day.

Try it at home! What will you discover?
WARNING: ASK A GROWN-UP FIRST!
Experiment with different coverings for your box.

"Do you think you're getting closer to inventing a time machine, then?" Lottie asked Al.

"I am!" grinned Al. "It'll be **AWESOME!** Mum'll be so much happier if we can take her back to a time when Dad was alive."

"Won't that mean we have to go back to being five years old?" Lottie asked Al.

"No, we'll go back with her at the age we are now," Al said confidently. "I'm not worried about that. What I'm worried about is — water!"

Water Shortage

"Why do you need water?" Lottie asked.

"For the splash down!" said Al.

"Splash down?" Lottie sounded puzzled.

"Yes. I haven't worked out where the time machine will land. Since over half the Earth's surface is water, it could splash down in the duck pond, or a lake or in the ocean! I have to know that it will land safely."

"There's no water around. There's a drought," Lottie reminded Al. "We should be saving water to help the garden wildlife!"

LOTTIE'S TOP TIPS:
How to save water and
help garden wildlife
during a drought

Wash fruit and veg in a bowl rather than running them under the tap. Tip this water into a shallow plastic container and put it out for birds and wildlife to drink and bathe in. Add a brick or a stick so animals that fall in can climb out.

Don't throw away washing-up water or bathwater. Use it to water one small patch of ground in the garden. This encourages worms to come to the surface. They make juicy snacks for wildlife!

Make a small hollow in the ground. Keep it damp to make a refuge for frogs and toads.

Nice hole!

Toadally awesome!

"I need to find out if a foil-covered time-machine capsule will float in water." Al picked up his box. "I'll try it in the kitchen sink."

"I'll help! Mum's saving the washing-up water to put on the roses, so we can use that. But that box will never fit in the sink," Lottie pointed out.

"You're right," Al agreed. "We need a big area of water to test it. Like the paddling pool."

"But we can't fill the paddling pool. There's a ban on using hosepipes, remember?" Lottie reminded him. "We've got to conserve water."

Just then, there was a happy whistling from next door's garden and a head popped over the fence.

"Lovely day!" Their neighbour Mr Good greeted them. "I've made some homemade lemonade. Would you like some?"

"Yes, please!" Al and Lottie chorused.

Mr Good handed a bottle of lemonade and two straws over the fence.

"Thanks!" Al and Lottie stood in the shade next to Einstein and took it in turns to take sips of the cold refreshing drink. "It's delicious!" they told Mr Good.

Einstein got up and sniffed at the bottle. He raised a hairy eyebrow. *Atchoo!* he sneezed and turned his head away in disgust.

Mr Good smiled. "He doesn't like lemons, then. Precious hates them too."

Einstein pricked up his ears and raised both eyebrows at the mention of the cat's name.

"Mildred doesn't allow lemons in the house in case they upset Precious," Mr Good went on. "That's why I'm

making lemonade while she's out . . ."
He gave the twins a worried look.

"We won't tell!" Lottie smiled. "How
is Precious doing in this heat? Einstein's
just lying around in a heap. He wouldn't
have the energy to chase Precious today
if she walked right in front of his nose!"

"Oh, Precious loves the sunshine!"
Mr Good replied. "And so do I. It's a
great day for pegging out the washing!"
He disappeared from view.

Al and Lottie peeped over the fence.
Precious was basking in the sunshine
in the middle of the Goods' garden.
They watched as Mr Good hung out

the washing. A lot of it was underwear.

"Look!" Lottie whispered. "Mrs Good's knickers all have cats on them!"

"They're all different sorts and colours. The cats, I mean." Al giggled.

The twins ducked down as Mr Good picked up the empty washing basket.

"Enjoy the sunshine, Precious. Your mummy will be so happy to find everything clean and dry when she gets home!" they heard him say.

There was a loud purr . . . purr . . . purrr . . . purrrr in reply. Then the Goods' back door clicked shut as Mr Good went back inside.

AWESOME SCIENCE FACT:
KNICKER WATER

EVAPORATION: Wet knickers dry best in hot sunshine, because water evaporates quickly and turns into a gas called water vapour.

COLLECTION: Water is collected in lakes, rivers, streams, icebergs and the sea.

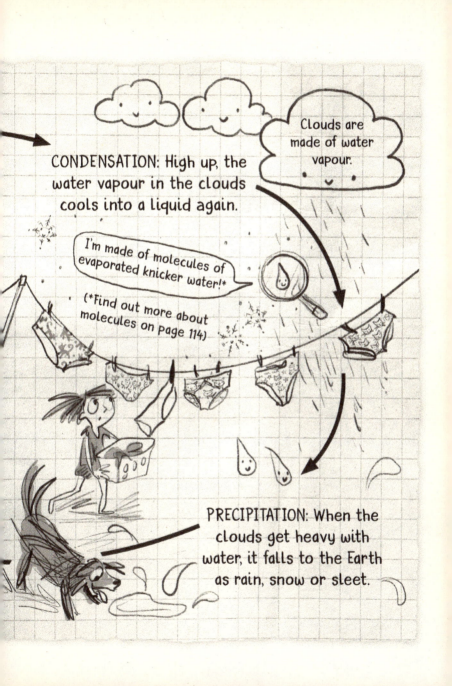

Lottie passed Al the lemonade bottle.

"Have you ever seen Mrs Good with a smile on her face?" she wondered.

Al shook his head as he sucked at the lemonade. He took the straw out of his mouth and stared at it. "I have an awesome idea!" he exclaimed. "We can use our straws to make a siphon. We'll siphon the dishwater out of the sink into the paddling pool . . . "

"Whaaa-t?" Lottie looked puzzled.

"A siphon is a tube that moves a liquid from one place to another. Watch this!"

Al took a pencil out of his pocket. He pushed the pointy part of the pencil into the short end of Lottie's straw to widen it. Next, Al inserted the long end of his straw into Lottie's straw. Holding up the lemonade bottle, he stuck one end of the straw tube into it and sucked hard on the other end. As soon as the straw was full of lemonade, he stopped sucking and bent it at the bendy bit so it looked like an upside-down V. Sticky lemonade began to flow onto the ground.

"Once a siphon starts, it keeps flowing," he said, as the lemonade poured out of the end of the straw.

"Don't waste that lemonade!"
Lottie protested.

"I won't. I'm just demonstrating."
Al pinched the end of the straw to
stop the flow. "All we need are a few
more straws, then we can siphon the

washing-up water from the sink out of the window into the paddling pool!"

"There's a box of straws in the kitchen cupboard." Lottie grinned. "I'll go and get them."

Al flapped away a wasp that had settled on the spilled lemonade. "The great thing about siphoning water," he said, "is that it won't make any mess at all!"

Scummy Water

A tube of straws stretched from the Boffins' kitchen sink and out of the kitchen window. The end dangled above the padding pool, which the twins had dragged under the window.

"That's an awesome siphon!" Al sighed proudly.

It had taken ages to carefully connect and tape the straws together so that each join was airtight.

"I can't wait to see if it works!" Lottie went inside and held one end of the straw siphon in the dishwater.

Al stood with the other end over the paddling pool and sucked on the straw as hard as he could.

"Suck harder," Lottie encouraged.

Al's face went purple with the effort, but then all of a sudden, his mouth filled with scummy water.

"Yuuurgh!" Al spluttered, spitting it out. "It works!" he cheered, as water started flowing into the pool.

Einstein pricked up his ears and

trotted over. He peered at the trickle of soapy, scummy water, gave it a lick and wrinkled his muzzle in disgust.

The water stopped flowing.

"What's up?" Al called to Lottie. "Is your end still in the sink?"

"Yep," Lottie replied. "But there's all sorts of disgusting stuff in this water. I'm trying to keep the big bits away from the end of the straw, but something must've got through and got stuck. You'll have to suck it out!"

Al sucked and sucked until – pop! Something shot into his mouth. He spat it into his hand. It was a tiny pea.

Al flapped his hand about and the pea fell into the paddling pool.

Einstein leaned over the edge and daintily picked it out with his teeth. **GULP!** it disappeared down his throat.

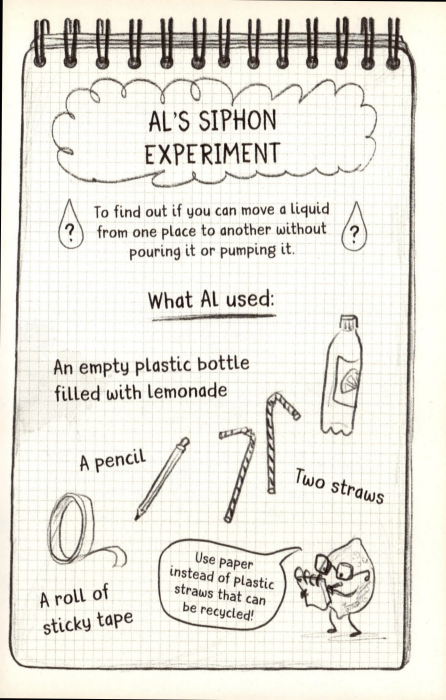

What Al did:

Al made the straws into one long tube (a siphon). Here's how:

1. Al carefully pushed the pointy end of a pencil into the short end of the first straw to make it flare out slightly.

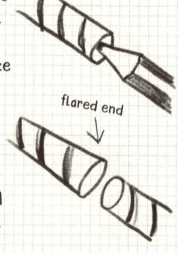

flared end

2. He pushed the long end of the other straw into the flared end of the first one.

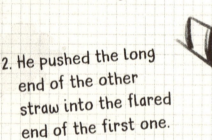

Tip: Tape the join together to stop the straws from falling apart or leaking air or water.

sticky tape

3. Al held up the lemonade bottle. He inserted the short end of the straw tube into it, and bent the other end into an upside-down V shape.

4. Al sucked on the long end of the straw tube – hard! This started the siphon.

5. When the straw siphon was full of liquid, Al stopped sucking. The lemonade flowed from the bottle onto the grass. (Use a bowl if you are experimenting inside.)

Try it at home! What will you discover?
WARNING: ASK A GROWN-UP FIRST! If you don't have lemonade, use CLEAN drinking water. To see the water going through the siphon clearly, try adding food colouring!

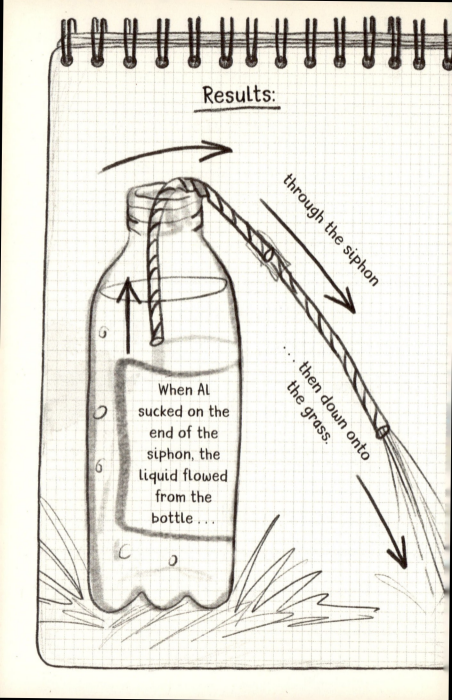

Results:

When Al sucked on the end of the siphon, the liquid flowed from the bottle . . .

through the siphon

. . . then down onto the grass.

Observations:

1. The siphon works because the level of the lemonade liquid inside the bottle is higher than the end of the siphon.

2. Water also flowed from the kitchen sink to the paddling pool because the sink is higher than the pool.

3. If it hadn't got blocked with bits of food, the siphon would have continued to work until the sink was empty.

Scientists don't agree about which forces make siphons work: Is it air pushing down on the surface of the water, then pushing it up the straw? Or is it gravity pulling water molecules* down, like a chain? Or both? WILL YOU GROW UP TO BE THE SCIENTIST WHO EXPLAINS IT?

*Find out more about molecules on page 114.

The siphon started up again, then stopped.

"There's another blockage," Al groaned. "This will take ages. Let's use Mum's bucket — the one she uses to mop the floors. You fill it, and pass it out of the window to me."

"This is much quicker," Lottie agreed, as she scooped water out of the sink into the bucket. She handed it out of the window. The handle caught on the tap, but Al gave it a hard pull and it freed itself.

In no time at all, they transferred all the scummy dishwater from the sink into the paddling pool.

Al grinned. He knew that the drops on the window sill would evaporate before Mum could see them. Plus there was enough water in the pool to check if his foil-covered box would float.

 AWESOME WATER FACTS:
70 percent of the Earth's surface is covered in water, but only a tiny part is fresh water that we can use: 97 percent of all water on Earth is salt water. Two percent of the fresh water is locked up in ice. That means there's just one percent for us to use.

There was a sudden

SPLASH!

Einstein was in the pool! He lay down with a happy sigh. The yucky dishwater splattered as he wagged his tail.

"We'll have to get him out of the pool so we can do the flotation experiment," Al said.

"But he's loving it!" Lottie giggled.

"It's perking him up. It would be cruel to disturb him right away!"

"OK," said Al. "Let's try out another water experiment that I read about in Great Grandpa Boffin's science book. "Remember we did all sorts of eggsperiments that involved gravity?"

"How could I forget?" Lottie grinned.

"Well, this experiment involves a different force called centripetal force . . ." Al's eyes shone.

"Sentry-peet-al force? I've never heard of it." Lottie frowned. "Why do you need to experiment with that?"

"It's really important to understand

the forces that my time machine might have to deal with as it goes through time and space," Al explained. "And all this experiment needs is a bucket of water and a bit of rope . . ."

"I'll fetch my old skipping rope!" said Lottie.

AWESOME SCIENCE FACT:
CENTRIPETAL FORCE

In a book published in 1687, Isaac Newton explained that a moving object will continue to move in a straight line unless a force acts upon it.

When centripetal force acts on an object, it's as if an invisible rope were pulling it to move in a circle instead of a straight line. On a roundabout, centripetal force keeps you spinning round in a circle. To make sure you don't fly off your seat, you have to hold on tight to the centre, which acts like the invisible rope.

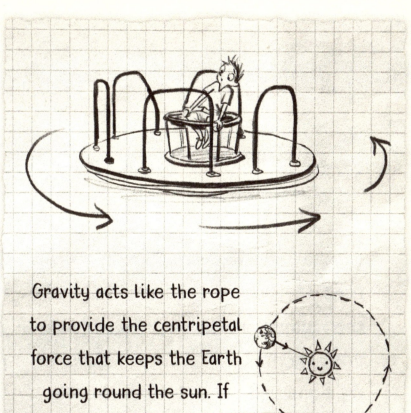

Gravity acts like the rope to provide the centripetal force that keeps the Earth going round the sun. If gravity broke, Earth would whizz off into Space.

Water Power

Einstein watched suspiciously as Al filled the bucket a quarter full with the scummy water from the paddling pool. He doubled up Lottie's skipping rope and tied the ends to the handle.

"I need the rope short so I can spin it round. Centripetal force will keep the water in the bucket. Like when clothes in a washing machine get stuck to the sides of the drum when it's on the spin cycle."

"Oh and like how you feel as if you're pushed outwards when you're on a roundabout," said Lottie.

She thought for a moment. "But when the washing machine stops spinning, the clothes fall to the bottom." She frowned.

"I'll stop the bucket, carefully," Al reassured her. He held the end of the skipping rope tightly with both hands so the bucket swung just above the ground.

"Here goes . . ." he said, making rapid circles with his arms so that the bucket spun round and round like a wheel in front of him.

"It works!" he exclaimed happily. "Look, no water is spilling out!"

WOOF!

There was a sudden loud bark.
Precious was tiptoeing along the garden
fence between the Boffins'
and the Goods' houses!

Einstein leapt out of the paddling pool. A large soggy doggy barged into Al, making the rope fly out of his hands. The bucket full of scummy water

arced through the air and over the fence into the Goods' garden.

"**MANGLED MOLECULES!**" exclaimed Al.

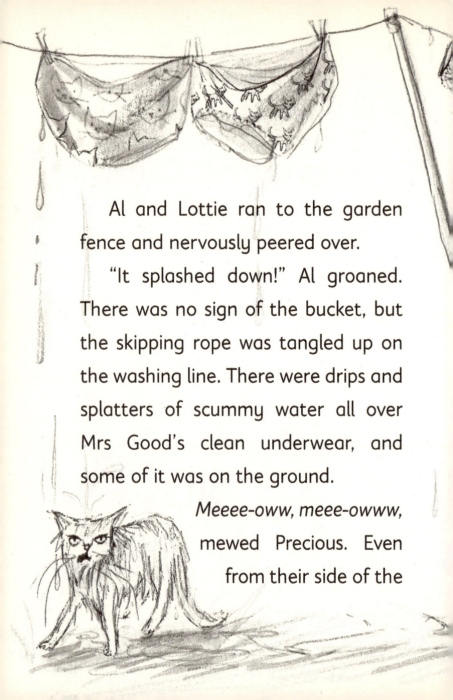

Al and Lottie ran to the garden fence and nervously peered over.

"It splashed down!" Al groaned. There was no sign of the bucket, but the skipping rope was tangled up on the washing line. There were drips and splatters of scummy water all over Mrs Good's clean underwear, and some of it was on the ground.

Meeee-oww, meee-owww, mewed Precious. Even from their side of the

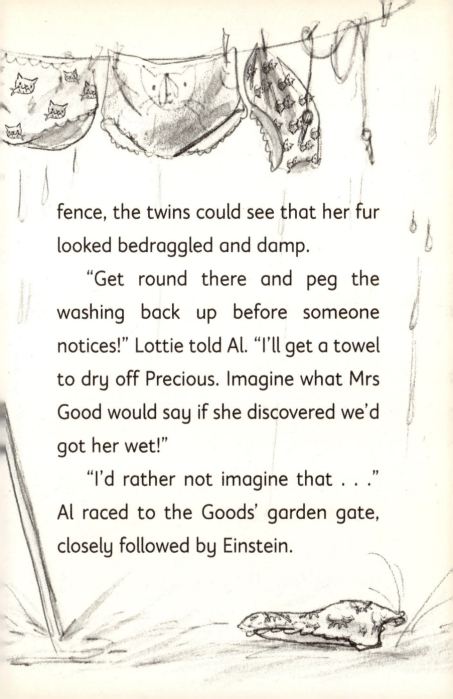

fence, the twins could see that her fur looked bedraggled and damp.

"Get round there and peg the washing back up before someone notices!" Lottie told Al. "I'll get a towel to dry off Precious. Imagine what Mrs Good would say if she discovered we'd got her wet!"

"I'd rather not imagine that . . ." Al raced to the Goods' garden gate, closely followed by Einstein.

By the time Lottie
arrived with the towel, there
was no sign of Precious.

"Maybe she'll dry off if she stays
out in the sun," Lottie said hopefully.

"We should've made sure Einstein
stayed in our garden," Al sighed,
flicking a bit of old carrot off a pair
of Mr Good's boxer shorts. "He scared
her off." He held a pair of Mrs Good's
knickers at arm's length as he pegged
it back on the line.

Lottie helped Al peg up the rest of
the washing. They were just finishing

when Einstein's ears pricked up. He tilted his head to one side.

Al and Lottie looked at one another and listened hard.

"It's a car," said Lottie, picking up the towel. "Einstein knows the sound of Mrs Good's car! She's on her way back. Quick, let's get out of here!"

Al grabbed the skipping rope and they raced back home.

"Phew!" he gasped, as they closed the kitchen door behind them. He was feeling all hot and bothered. "That was close! I could do with an ice-cream."

"Me too!" said Lottie. She pushed her sweaty hair out of her eyes. "I'll go and ask Mum."

Lottie glanced at Einstein as she opened the door of the shop. He had curled up in a damp heap in the corner of the kitchen, with his back to them. It was almost as if he was hiding something.

AL'S WATER BUCKET EXPERIMENT

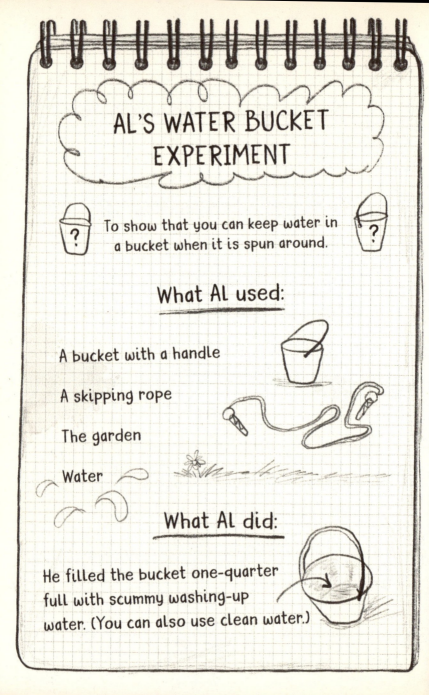

To show that you can keep water in a bucket when it is spun around.

What Al used:

A bucket with a handle

A skipping rope

The garden

Water

What Al did:

He filled the bucket one-quarter full with scummy washing-up water. (You can also use clean water.)

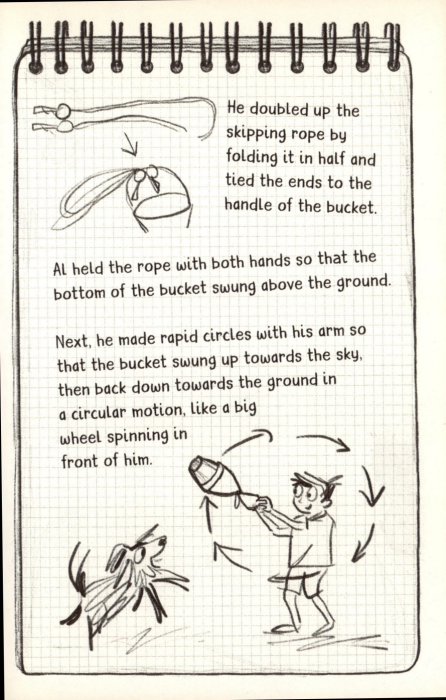

He doubled up the skipping rope by folding it in half and tied the ends to the handle of the bucket.

Al held the rope with both hands so that the bottom of the bucket swung above the ground.

Next, he made rapid circles with his arm so that the bucket swung up towards the sky, then back down towards the ground in a circular motion, like a big wheel spinning in front of him.

Results:

When Al swung the bucket quickly round in a circle, the water stayed inside.

When Al let go of the rope, the bucket flew off in a straight line. Water spilled out.

SPLOSH!

Observations

1. When Al swung his bucket in a circle, the rope stretched taught. This tension created a centripetal force that kept the bucket spinning round and the water inside.

2. When the bucket stopped spinning, gravity pulled it down so water sloshed everywhere. Stop yours carefully!

3. It's best not to let go of the end of the rope suddenly.

OOPS!

4. If your time machine is caught in a centripetal force in outer space, gravity is probably pulling you into the orbit of an alien planet. (Watch out!)

TIP: don't let the bucket hit the ground or the water will splosh out and you'll get very soggy!

Try it at home! What will you discover?
WARNING: ASK A GROWN-UP FIRST! Be sure the area around you is clear so that no-one gets hit when you spin the bucket. Stop the bucket carefully. IT COULD GET MESSY...

Ice Scream

"Mum says the shop has run out of ice-cream," Lottie reported when she came back.

"Never mind," said Al. "I'm a scientist. I know how to make some! We just need a couple of zip-up food bags, ice, milk, cream, sugar, salt . . . and maybe some vanilla essence."

"Salty ice-cream doesn't sound

very nice," Lottie said, as Al rummaged through the kitchen cupboards, the fridge and the freezer and helped himself to what he needed.

"The salt's not for taste. It's to bring down the temperature and make the milk and cream freeze more quickly," Al explained. He poured a small tub of cream into a bag.

He handed it to Lottie, then used the cream tub to measure the same amount of milk. He tipped it into the bag, along with a quarter tub of sugar and a few drops of vanilla essence. Then he zipped it up and gave it back to Lottie to hold.

"The second bag's for ice and salt . . ." Al threw in two tubs of crushed ice and half a tub of salt.

He gave it a shake.

"Now, we put the bag with the cream mix inside the other bag, hold it at the top with one hand, and gently squish it all together with the other!

That'll mangle the molecules!" Al put on some oven gloves.

Lottie reached out to touch the bag.

"Brrr. That's cold!" She grabbed a dishcloth to wrap around her hands so she could have a go at squishing it too. "How long do we need to do this?"

"About fifteen minutes," Al said, looking at his watch.

"It's already going a bit solid," Lottie grinned.

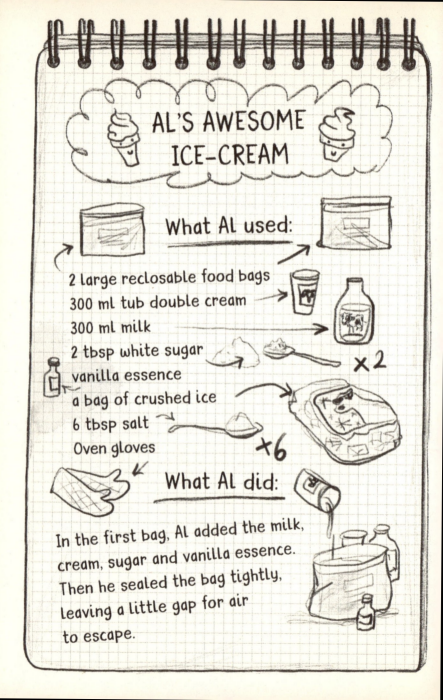

AL'S AWESOME ICE-CREAM

What Al used:

2 large reclosable food bags
300 ml tub double cream
300 ml milk
2 tbsp white sugar
vanilla essence
a bag of crushed ice
6 tbsp salt
Oven gloves

×2

×6

What Al did:

In the first bag, Al added the milk, cream, sugar and vanilla essence. Then he sealed the bag tightly, leaving a little gap for air to escape.

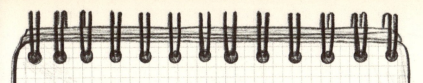

Al filled the second bag half-full with crushed ice and added the salt.

Al placed the bag with the cream mix inside the bag with the ice and salt and closed it up tightly.

Putting on oven gloves, he gently squished it on the kitchen counter for 15 minutes until the cream mix turned solid.

He carefully separated out the bags, washed off the salt and scooped out the ice-cream.

← YUM!

Results

Squishing the mix combined the cream, sugar and milk into a smooth mixture. It froze to make some yummy ice-cream!

Observations

1. When you surround the cream mixture with the ice-salt mixture, it lowers the temperature.

2. As it freezes, the cream mix changes from liquid to solid and makes 'ice' cream.

3. It might be nice to mix in bits of fruit - or chocolate!

TIP: Put your ice-cream in the freezer for a bit to make it more solid.

Try it at home! What will you discover?
WARNING: ASK A GROWN-UP FIRST!
IT COULD GET MESSY . . .

Al put the bags in the sink and carefully separated them. He grabbed a tea towel and brushed off the salt.

Lottie found two spoons. "I'm so hot," she said. "I can't wait to taste it!"

Al opened the ice-cream bag and they dipped in.

"Yum!" Lottie exclaimed.

"We should give some to Mr Good to thank him for the lemonade."

"Yes, he loves homemade things!" Al spooned some of the delicious ice-cream into a plastic bowl.

Lottie glanced at the empty ice-cream bag and the bag full of salty mush in the sink. "Better clear these up before Mum sees," she said. "We can re-use the bags."

She turned on the tap. "That's odd. The tap's a bit wobbly . . ."

Lottie rinsed out the bags then went to turn off the water. "**I CAN'T TURN THE TAP OFF!**" she gasped.

Al reached across. "Neither can I!" he said in dismay.

"It must've broken when the handle of the bucket got caught on it!" Lottie cried. "We have to turn it off! We're wasting water."

Al grabbed a roll of clingfilm and wrapped it round and round the end of the tap.

"That'll hold," he said confidently, but as they watched, a layer of the stretchy plastic film began to form a bubble . . .

The bubble burst. Water splattered everywhere.

POP!

"We need something else to stuff in the tap," Al cried, glancing round the kitchen. "Einstein's treat sticks are about the right size . . ."

Al stuffed one into the end of the tap. "There, that fits perfectly!"

"Uh-oh," Lottie warned. "The water's pushing it out . . ."

There was a sploshy slurping noise and the rubbery snack bounced off the sink and onto the kitchen floor. Einstein bounded over and gobbled it up.

Al pressed the palm of his hand over the end of the tap.

"That works," Lottie sighed with relief.

"But I can't keep it up for long," Al warned. "My hand's going numb. We need something else to wrap around the tap."

"Something stronger than clingfilm. A tea towel, maybe."

"The tea towel's not long enough to tie, unless we rip it," Lottie said. "Mum won't like that. Hey, what's that over there?"

She went to investigate a pile of soggy pink cloth in the corner where Einstein had been sitting.

"Oh, no!" Lottie gasped, holding it up for Al to see. It was well-sucked and soaked with doggy dribble, but it was still possible to make out the two leg holes . . . and the pattern of little grey cats on it.

"Mrs Good's knickers!" Lottie groaned. "Einstein must have found a pair and brought it in from next door. He's completely chewed off the elastic!"

"It's perfect for bunging up the tap!" Al said. "Quick! Twist it up a bit . . ."

Lottie twisted up one leg of the knickers. She stuffed it into the tap the instant Al took his hand away. Then Al tied it in place with the loose bits of elastic.

The garden gate creaked and there was a knock on the back door.

"Mrs Good!" Lottie gasped. "She mustn't see her knickers! Distract her!"

Al opened the door and Mrs Good thundered in. She was carrying her laundry basket.

"What have you two been up to?" she growled. "My clean washing is filthy! And some of it was pegged on the line upside down!!! Mr Good would never do that."

"Er . . . we saw it fall off the line so we pegged it back up," Lottie said. "We're sorry if it got a bit dirty, aren't we Al . . ."

"Very sorry." Al nodded. "We have just been making homemade ice-cream," he went on. "Would you

like to try some? Why don't you take it home so Mr Good can try it, too?" Al picked up the bowl.

"We forgot to put it in the freezer, so it's melted a bit," he explained.

He stepped forward to hand it to Mrs Good.

"OOOPS!"

Al yelled as his foot slipped on a puddle of water. The plastic bowl flew out of his hands and bounced on the kitchen floor.

Ice-cold ice-cream goo splattered up Mrs Good's legs.

"Eek!" she screamed, as
Einstein began to lick it off.
"Wish we had a time
machine!" Lottie muttered.

In Hot Water

Mrs Good whirled round the kitchen, trying to avoid Einstein's sloppy licks. She came to a sudden stop at the sink.

"What are my favourite knickers doing wrapped around your tap?!" she gasped, pulling at them. But Al had tied them on too well. The tap and the knickers came away in Mrs Good's hand.

A fountain of water gushed up from the hole where the tap had been.

It rained down on Mrs Good and the kitchen floor.

WHOOOOSH!

Mrs Good stood red-faced and dripping, clutching her soggy knickers as Einstein raced round and round her in circles, kicking up spray.

After what seemed like forever, she found her voice.

"Your mother needs to know about this!" she shouted, and she stomp-splished towards the shop door, clutching her soggy knickers.

"Oh dear," Lottie groaned.

"Quick!" Al said. "We have just about enough time to do the **SPLASH DOWN TEST!**"

Al raced outside and grabbed his foil-covered box. He held it above his head, then dropped it on the flooded kitchen floor.

SPLASH

The box bobbed up and down.

"It floats really well!" Al confimed.

"Einstein thinks we turned the kitchen into a padding pool for him!" Lottie laughed.

DOWN!

"My goodness! What have you been up to?" Mrs Boffin took one look at the state of the kitchen and dived into the cupboard beneath the sink. "There's a stopcock under here that turns the water off at the pipe!" she told the twins.

Al, Lottie and Einstein watched nervously as Mrs Boffin took Mrs Good's elbow and guided her to a chair at the kitchen table. Mum made two mugs of tea and sat down opposite Mrs Good.

"The twins . . . my, my best knickers . . ." Mrs Good began.

AWESOME WATER FACTS:

Water can exist in three states –
solid, liquid and gas – and they are
all found in your kitchen!

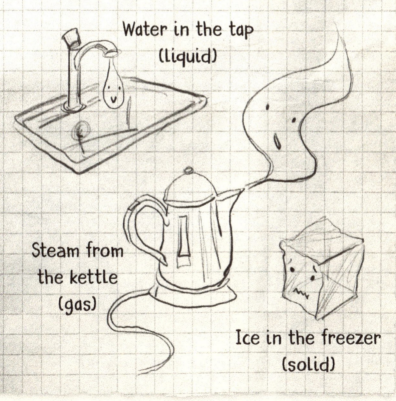

Water in the tap
(liquid)

Steam from
the kettle
(gas)

Ice in the freezer
(solid)

"I'm sure there's some explanation,"
Mum said, glaring at the twins.

"We're very sorry," Al and Lottie said together.

"Einstein must have pinched your knickers off your washing line, Mrs Good. We'll give you our pocket money so you can buy a new pair, won't we, Lottie?" Al said.

Lottie nodded in agreement.

Einstein's ears drooped. He looked very guilty.

Mum regarded them sternly. "Who broke the tap?" she asked. "I'll have to get a plumber in to fix it."

Mrs Good went pink. Maybe she was feeling a bit guilty about that, thought Al.

"Er . . . I did," Al said. "It was an accident." He glanced at Mrs Good. Was it his imagination, or did she look slightly relieved? "We were doing some awesome science experiments outside using leftover washing-up water," Al went on.

"So we wouldn't waste water," Lottie piped up.

"But we caught the handle of the bucket on the tap," Al explained. "The siphon was taking ages, you see . . ."

"Science again?" Mrs Boffin gave a tired smile. "I like to see you both taking after your dad and your Great Grandpa Boffin, but they never made as much mess as you!"

"Well," said Mrs Good, taking a sip of her tea. "At least it's only water this time. Mostly." She brushed a glob of melted ice-cream off her trousers. "I'd forgotten what it's like to have a nice cool paddle on a hot day."

Al, Lottie and Mrs Boffin looked at one another. They could hardly believe their ears.

Mum got to her feet. "Thank you for being so nice about it," she told Mrs Good. "But the twins need to clear up this water now, before it damages the floor. I'll get them the mop and bucket."

The twins exchanged a horrified glance. They'd forgotten all about the bucket!

Mum spotted the looks on their faces.

"Did something happen to my bucket when you were using it for your experiments?" she asked ominously.

There was a tap on the door. It was Mr Good. He was holding a bucket in one hand and clutching a damp and upset-looking cat to his chest with the other.

Einstein's ears pricked up.

Precious mewed piteously.

"Precious! What have they done to you?" Mrs Good rose to her feet, still clutching her soggy knickers. She cradled her cat. "We'll get to the bottom of this!" she promised fiercely.

WOOF!

Einstein threw himself at Precious and knocked Mrs Good off her feet.

Mrs Good, Precious and Einstein thrashed around in the scuzzy water on the kitchen floor.

SPLASH!

"Mildred!" Mr Good waded in to the rescue, and slipped over.

Einstein howled as Precious's paw
scratched his nose.

OWWWLL!

Al glanced at Lottie and at the foil-covered box that was still managing to stay afloat. "If only it was a real time-machine capsule," he sighed.

"Maybe it will help if you tell them

you'll stop experimenting," Lottie whispered.

Al gave her a disbelieving look. "No way!" he said. "I'm a scientist! Scientists **NEVER** give up!"

AWESOME SCIENCE FACT:
MOLECULES!

Everything, including you, is made up of atoms or molecules. You have too many to count! Molecules are made of two or more tinier parts called atoms that stick together to form a group. For example, a water molecule is made up of 2 hydrogen atoms and 1 oxygen atom, like this:

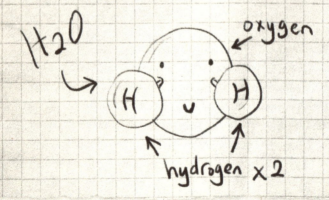

Molecules are tiny! A single drop
of water may contain over
10,000,000,000,000,000,000,000
water molecules.

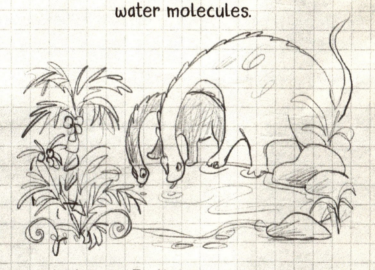

Water on Earth has been around
since life began. So the water you
drink could contain molecules that
dinosaurs drank!

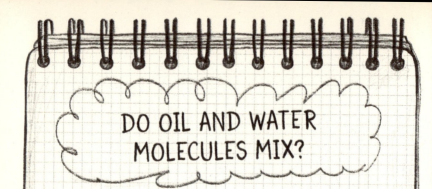

DO OIL AND WATER MOLECULES MIX?

To see molecules in action try this:

1. Fill a glass jar half-full with water.
   Now, add four tablespoons of oil.
   Put on the lid. Shake. What happens?

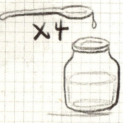

Oil molecules are only attracted to oil
molecules, while water molecules are
only attracted to water molecules. Oil
and water will tend to separate after
being shaken. Ordinary oil is less dense/
heavy than water so it will float.

2. Now, add a squirt of washing-up liquid and a few drops of food colouring. Put on the lid. Shake the jar again and watch what happens.

When you add a squirt of washing-up liquid, the oil and water will mix. This is because detergent molecules are attracted to *both* oil and water molecules. So washing-up liquid is great for cleaning greasy dishes!

 WARNING! ASK A GROWN-UP FIRST. IT COULD GET MESSY!

RAIN IN A JAR

To discover how rain works.

What you will need:

Empty glass jar
Shaving cream
Food colouring (blue or another colour will work too)
Water
A dropper

1. Fill the jar two-thirds full with water.

2. Add shaving cream on top to look like a cloud.

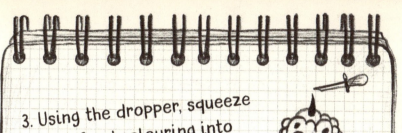

3. Using the dropper, squeeze blue food colouring into different parts of the shaving foam cloud – like 'rain'.

4. Watch what happens inside the jar!

How does it work?

When the clouds get too full of water (the blue food colouring), it falls as rain.

The rain that plops on your head could contain molecules of evaporated knicker water!

Read more of **AL'S AWESOME SCIENCE** adventures and have fun doing more experiments at home!

Al is experimenting to find the best shape for his time-machine capsule . . . with eggs! But a nosy neighbour and her cat Precious lands him and his twin sister Lottie in a very sticky situation.

COMING IN OCTOBER 2018!

It's the twins' birthday and Al and his friends are experimenting to find out how to blast off his time machine into outer Space. Trouble is, fiddling with balloons and homemade rockets is very messy!